Attitudes of Gratitude

GUIDED JOURNAL

M. J. Ryan

Conari Press

First published in 2009 by
Red Wheel/Weiser, LLC
500 Third Street, Suite 230
San Francisco, CA 94107
www.redwheelweiser.com

The text was adapted from *Attitudes of Gratitude,* originally published in 1999 by
Conari Press, ISBN: 978-1-57324-149-6

ISBN: 978-1-57324-451-0

Typeset in Perpetua and Gigi
Cover and text design by Jessica Dacher

Manufactured in China
MD
10 9 8 7 6 5 4 3 2 1

If you look to others for fulfillment,
    you will never truly be fulfilled.
If your happiness depends on money,
    you will never be happy with yourself.
Be content with what you have;
    rejoice in the way things are.
When you realize there is nothing lacking,
    the whole world belongs to you.
—LAO TZU

Gratitude is not just the key. It's a magic key — all you need to do is use it, and the world is suddenly transformed into a beautiful wonderland in which you are invited to play. That's because, like most of the great spiritual truths, gratitude is stunningly simple. This is not to say that an attitude of gratitude is necessarily easy to practice. All kinds of distractions and negative attitudes, many of them learned early in our lives, may get in the way. But all you really have to do is make a commitment to do it, and the magic will be yours.

One of the incredible truths about gratitude is that it is impossible to feel both the positive emotion of thankfulness and a negative emotion such as anger or fear at the same time. Gratitude births only positive feelings — love, compassion, joy, and hope. As we focus on what we are thankful for, negative feelings simply melt away.

Gratitude unlocks the fullness of life.

A Grateful Heart

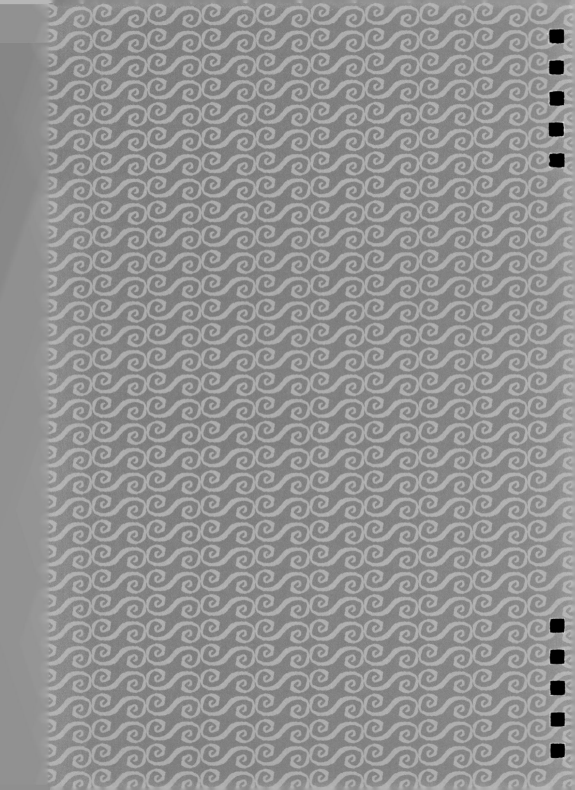

"It turns what we have into enough, and more. It turns denial into acceptance, chaos into order, confusion into clarity.... Gratitude makes sense of our past, brings peace for today, and creates a vision for tomorrow." ——MELODY BEATTIE

Take a few minutes to reflect on a happy moment in your life that stands out for you. Experience it again: see the scene, hear the sounds, feel the sensations.

What was it about that moment that stays with you?

Was gratitude a part of it?

Gratitude is the mother of joy.

"Joy is prayer —— Joy is strength —— Joy is love —— Joy is a net of love by which you can catch souls. She gives most who gives with joy."

—— MOTHER TERESA

Make a list of all that you have accomplished today.

Celebrate each feat, no matter its size.

"The invariable mark of wisdom is to see the miraculous in the common." —RALPH WALDO EMERSON

Gratitude makes us young. ♡

You don't have to lose the happiness or juiciness
of youth. Tap into your sense of gratitude, and you'll feel
like a small child seeing the world for the first time.
How does gratitude change your perspective?

"Begin today. Declare out loud to the Universe that you are willing to let go of struggle and eager to learn through joy."

——SARAH BAN BREATHNACH

Gratitude makes you feel good.

What about myself am I grateful for?

When you live with a grateful heart, you'll see endless opportunities to give: a flower from the garden to a coworker, a kind word to our child, a visit to an old person. You will know what to do.

Notice those around you to whom gratitude comes easily and how easy it is to be around them. Name them.

"Each day I learn more than I teach." —VIRGINIA CHURCH

Instead of climbing mindlessly to some undefined peak of accomplishment, make a list of the wonderful things happening in your day-to-day life. What wonderful thing happened to you today?

Gratitude reminds us to be like plants, which turn toward, not away, from the light.

"Let us embrace the past with remembrance and the future with longing." —KAHIL GIBRAN

The Gifts of Gratitude

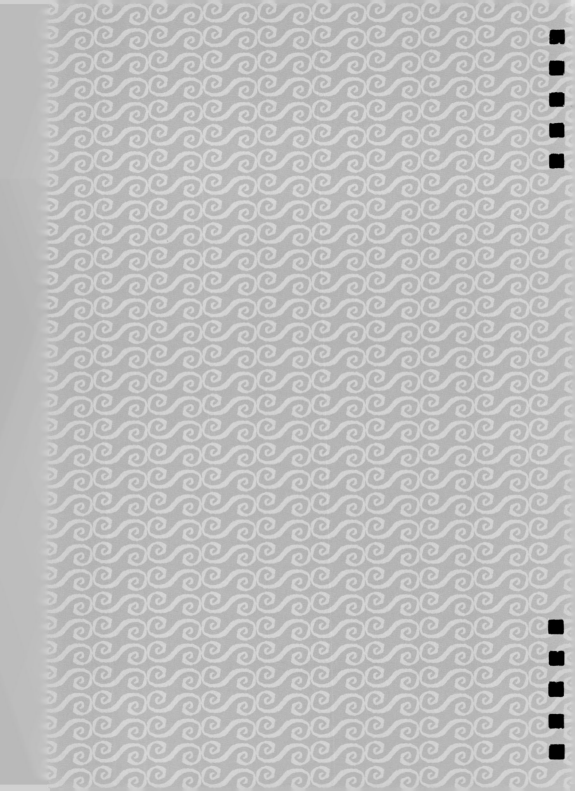

Gratitude opens your heart.

Gratefulness is only experienced in the moments in which you open our heart to life — to the beauty of the moment, to the possibility of surprise in the next.

Imagine a person does something kind for you, even a very small thing — like holding a door open. When you say "Thank you" and really mean it, rather than saying it out of social convention, your heart instinctively opens to the person. In that moment, you experience connection with one another, even if you never lay eyes on each other again.

Openheartedness takes courage. It requires enough trust in the goodness of other people and the universe at large that we can put aside our self-protectiveness—that voice that says, "I am not going to be grateful for what I am receiving right now because it's too scary to risk getting hurt"—and take a leap of faith to acknowledge that we have received a gift.

Do you want to live in seeming safety, shut inside the shell of your individuality, unwilling to experience deep and abiding connections with others, or are you willing to risk, over and over, having your heart broken open to the beauty and the pain of life?

When do you experience an open heart?

What are the conditions that foster your willingness
to open your heart?

What risks are you willing to take?

"The more light you allow within you, the brighter the world you live in will be." —SHAKTI GAWAIN

Gratitude is an inner light that you can use to illumine your soul.

When you see the glass as half-full rather than half-empty,
you notice what is there rather than dwelling on what is not.
Do you approach life with hope and optimism?

Gratitude promotes health.

"Feelings of gratitude release positive endorphins throughout the body." —SHARON HUFFMAN

Gratitude cures perfectionism.

"A point worth pondering: Upon completing the Universe, the Great Creator pronounced it 'very good.' Not 'perfect.'" — SARAH BAN BREATHNACH

"If there is to be any peace it will come through being, not having." —HENRY MILLER

Gratitude keeps you current.

"That it will never come again is what makes life so sweet."
— EMILY DICKINSON

As you allow yourself to open to the fullness of gratitude, the past and future fade away and you become more alive in the present moment. How do you keep yourself grounded in the present?

"Our work-a-day lives are filled with opportunities to bless others. The power of a single glance or an encouraging smile must never be underestimated." —G. RICHARD RIEGER

Gratitude begets generosity which begets gratitude which begets generosity.

The more you feel
grateful, the stronger is the
impulse toward giving.

The more you give, the more you get—love, friendship, a sense of purpose and accomplishment; even, sometimes, material wealth. What do you give to your loved ones?

"When I feel the joy of receiving a gift, my heart nudges me to join creation's ballet, the airy dance of giving and receiving, and getting and giving again." —LEWIS SMEDES

Gratitude *joins us to all life.*

Gratitude connects
us to spirit.

"If the only prayer you say in your whole life is 'thank you,' that would suffice." ——MEISTER ECKHART

Gratitude opens us to
moments of grace.

"Nobody can conceive or imagine all the wonders there are unseen and unseeable in the world." ——FRANCIS P. CHURCH

How has gratitude brought more grace into your life?

Has has gratitude made you feel more fulfilled? How?

How can you teach gratitude to others?

The
Attitudes

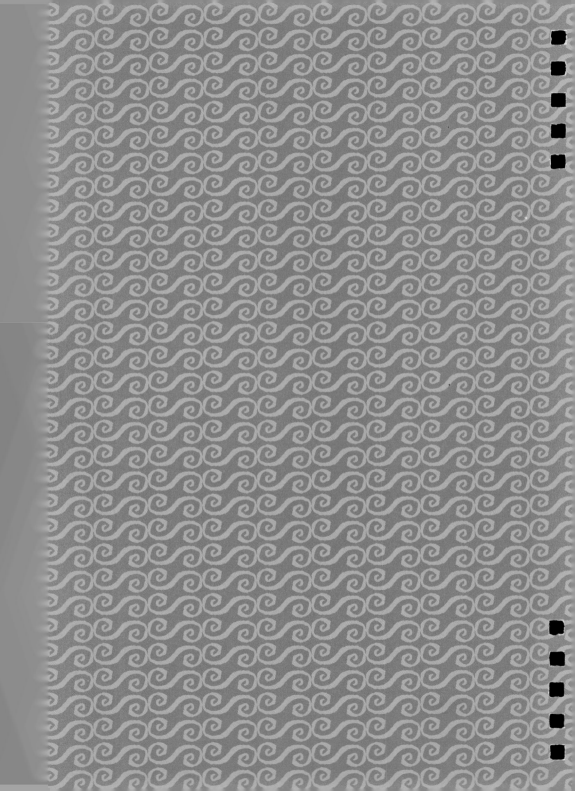

"The most powerful agent of growth and transformation is something much more basic than any technique: a change of heart."
— JOHN WELWOOD

The next step on the journey is to look at the attitudes of gratitude—those beliefs that foster a sense of thankfulness. Attitudes are the underpinnings of action; as John Welwood implies, you can't change on the outside until and unless you transform your thinking, the way you imagine yourself, and your reality. The good news is that you really can decide to see the glass as half-full rather than half-empty, and that decision will have profoundly positive effects not only on your happiness and that of those around you, but on the way your whole life unfolds.

"Einstein was asked what he thought the most important question was that a human being needed to answer. His reply was 'Is the universe friendly or not?'" — JOAN BORYSENKO

If you believe the Universe is friendly, then you feel that life is on your side, that good things will come your way, and that even when bad things happen they are bumps in the road designed to teach you to become more wise, more whole, more loving. What is your view of the Universe?

Let gratitude flow naturally.

"One's destination is never a place but rather a new way of looking at things." —HENRY MILLER

What are some of the ways that gratitude comes naturally

into your life?

"This is what binds all people and all creation together— the gratuity of the gift of being." —MATTHEW FOX

"Inside yourself or outside, you never have to change what you see — only the way you see it." —— THADDEUS GOLAS

Your attitudes are your mental stances, the positions you hold vis-à-vis life. Do you approach life with a positive or negative attitude?

When you consciously cultivate positive attitudes like love,

joy, and gratitude, you begin to "remake" the world.

The more loving you are, the
more love you feel in return.

The more joy you radiate, the more comes back your way.

How have you experienced this in your life?

The more thankful you are, the more
you experience the richness of spirit that
grateful feelings produce.

Attitude is the only disability.

Focus on the negative and descend into a spiral of negativity and gloom. Look at what's right in any given situation, and become a beacon of love and joy. How can you maintain a positive focus?

> *"The secret to life is to know when enough is enough."*
>
> ——DR. VINCENT RYAN

How do you cultivate a true and deep appreciation for what you have?

"Make it new." —EZRA POUND

It's OK to have good fortune. What are you blessed with?

When you can live as if it is always the first time,

you won't have to try to experience a sense

of gratitude. It will be there, automatically, as a

natural response to the beauty and the bounty.

"There are only two ways to live your life. One is as though nothing is a miracle. The other is as though everything is a miracle." —ALBERT EINSTEIN

Is it possible for us in this culture to truly and fully appreciate what we have been given without feeling guilty? If not, perhaps it is our responsibility to acknowledge our guilt, so that it doesn't block our willingness to be grateful.

"You are a child of the Universe no less than the trees and the stars; you have a right to be here." —— DESIDERATA

To experience gratitude, you
have to be aware that you've been
given something.

"It is up to you to illumine the earth." ——PHILIPPE VENSIER

If you want the habit of gratitude to grace your life, it is essential that you develop the belief that you are here on Earth to fulfill some purpose that only you can offer to the world. What is your purpose?

You are an **amazingly**
rare, totally irreplicable
individual with talents and
gifts that the world truly needs.

The more that you experience the truth of your uniqueness and beauty, the more you will feel gratitude for your particular gifts — and the more you will be able to deliver them. What unique gifts have you been blessed with?

How can you use these gifts for the greater good?

The Practices
of Gratitude—
Self

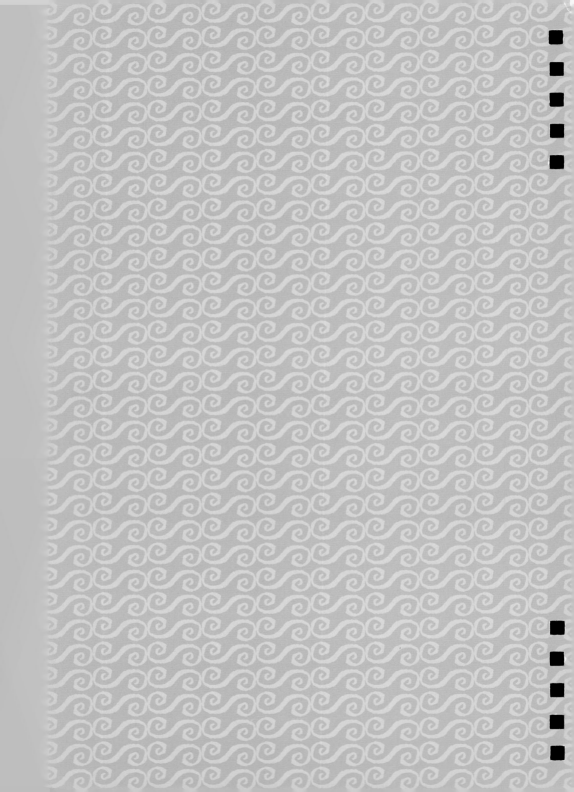

"Beginning to tune into even the minutest feelings of...
gratitude softens us.... If we begin to acknowledge
these moments and cherish them...then no
matter how fleeting and tiny this good heart may
seem, it will gradually, at its own speed, expand."
——PEMA CHÖDRÖN

In the next stage of your journey, you begin to put your attitudes into action. Here you don't just feel grateful; you express your feelings of gratefulness in a variety of ways that enrich your life and the lives of those around you. You truly ripen your soul, for it is easy to pay lip service to the idea of gratitude and not take the final step of embodying it. But when you begin to practice gratitude, you create a powerful resonance between your thoughts and actions, and your soul shines forth in all its brilliance.

start where you are.

"If you haven't got all the things you want, be grateful for the things you don't have that you don't want." —ANONYMOUS

A pessimist is someone who has exercised the muscles
of negativity until they are habitual, while an optimist is
a person who has developed thankfulness and a can-do
attitude until these are second nature. Which are you?

Developing the muscle of gratitude is just
like exercising any other: you have to practice
and repeat, or the muscle will wither.

Daily rituals really help cultivate gratitude.
Make a commitment to list ten things every day
that you are grateful for.

Choose gratefulness.

"As you wander on through life, sister/brother, whatever be your goal, keep your eye upon the donut, and not upon the hole."

— SIGN IN THE MAYFLOWER COFFEE SHOP, CHICAGO

Revel in the ordinary.

Pick an ordinary task, something you do every day, and decide that just for today, you will do it with awareness. How does it feel different?

When we focus on what we truly need, as opposed to
what we might like or want, life gets much simpler.
What do you really need?

*"Three grand essentials to happiness in this life are something
to do, something to love, and something to hope for."*
— JOSEPH ADDISON

*"There are many ways to victimize people.
One way is to convince them that they are victims."*

——KAREN HWANG

Nothing blocks feelings of gratitude more than anger and resentment. That's why the practice of gratitude requires the work of forgiveness. How can you work more forgiveness into your life?

Healing, in the form of acknowledging the grievance

and grieving the loss or wound, needs to happen first.

How are you healing yourself?

Practice wonderment.

"Oh, for the wonder that bubbles into my soul."

—— D. H. LAWRENCE

Don't compare.

"Life begets life. Energy creates energy. It is by spending oneself that one becomes rich." —SARAH BERNHARDT

Develop a good memory.

Do you like yourself? What are you grateful for about you?

"Gratitude is the memory of the heart; therefore, forget not to say often: I have all I ever enjoyed." —LYDIA CHILD

The
Practices —
Service

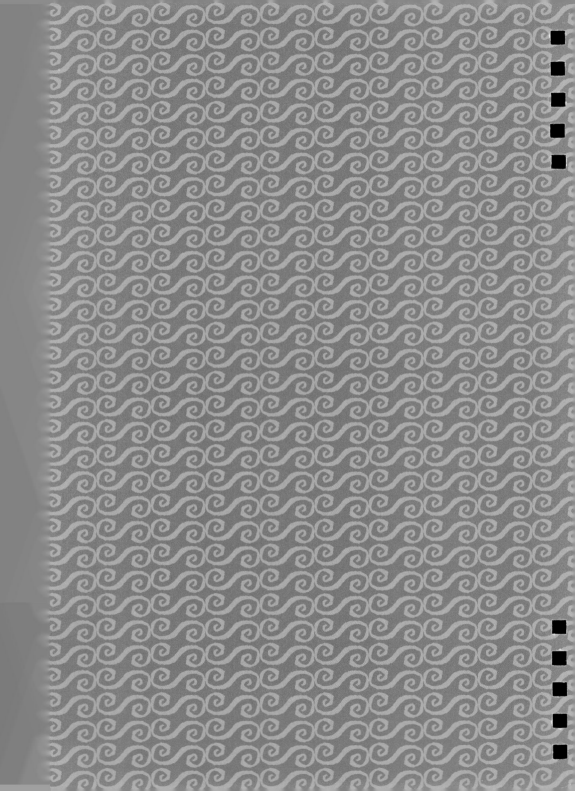

It is more blessed to give than receive.
—ACTS 20:35

One of the wonderful effects of gratitude is the desire to spread the joy around. You are aware you have received something wonderful, and you want to give back a measure of the bounty. There are all kinds of ways to do that, of course—from random acts of kindness, like letting the car that's trying to nose ahead of you in, to planned giving such as a charitable donation.

say "Thank You"
as often as possible.

"Let's feel the magic of those two little, big words, 'Thank you.'"

——ARDATH RODALE

Count the number of "Thank you's" you say during one day.

Could you say more?

Give thanks at meals.

"Before you taste anything, recite a blessing." — RABBI AKIVA

How can you teach gratitude to your young ones?

"Thank you for being."

—TRADITIONAL GREETING OF THE SENECA

There is no house like the house of belonging. —DAVID WHYTE

Honoring your connection to your ancestors gives you a sense
of belonging and wholeness. How do you honor your family?

Celebrate your
teachers.

"No matter what accomplishments you achieve, somebody helped you." —ALTHEA GIBSON

When you take the time to appreciate those who have been your greatest teachers, you not only express your thanks for the learning; you feel more connected to life as a whole. Who have you most learned from in your life?

Life is a journey on which you become more and more fully who you are meant to be. Who is that person?

"Choose thy love. Love thy choice."

—— GERMAN PROVERB

Live as if every day is your last.

Write down the ten hardest or most terrible things that ever
happened to you. As you look over the list, can you see the
gifts that each of them brought?

If this were your last day on Earth, what would you do?

If this were the last day on Earth of someone you loved,

what would you say to them?

"What amazes me is that before we can count we are taught to be grateful for what others do. As we are broken open by our experience, we begin to be grateful for what is, and if we live long enough and deep enough and authentically enough, gratitude becomes a way of life." —MARK NEPO